BIRDSEYE MATH SKILLS

Addition & Subtraction

Valerie E. Mock

Fearon Teacher Aids
a division of
David S. Lake Publishers
Belmont, California

Mastery Masters™ Blackline Masters

Produced by Ron Newcomer & Associates

ISBN-0-8224-0715-9

Printed in the United States of America.

1.9 8 7 6 5 4 3 2

CONTENTS

Introduction

A Birdseye View

Seeing Dots *adding and subtracting 2-digit numbers, without regrouping* 1
Flying with the Eagles *adding and subtracting 2- and 3-digit numbers, with regrouping* 2
Measuring Up *subtracting 2- and 3-digit numbers, with regrouping* 3
Spotting Golden Eagles *adding and subtracting 2- to 4-digit numbers, with regrouping* 4

Auto Racing

Repairing a Truck *adding 2- and 3-digit numbers, with regrouping* 5
Buying Auto Parts *adding 2- and 3-digit numbers, with regrouping (money)* 6
Setting New Records *using* greater than, less than, *and* equal to *with 2- and 3-digit numbers* 7
Designing a Race Car *adding 3-digit numbers, with regrouping (money)* 8
Earning Money *adding 2- and 3-digit numbers, with regrouping (money)* 9
Racing with Birdseye *adding and subtracting 2- to 4-digit numbers, without regrouping* 10
Indy 500 *subtracting 2- and 3-digit numbers, with regrouping* 11
African Car Safari *adding 2- to 4-digit numbers, with regrouping (money)* 12
Birdseye's Mail *adding 2- to 4-digit numbers, with regrouping* 13

Museum Fossils

Ice Age Animals *using* greater than, less than, *and* equal to *with 2- to 4-digit numbers* 14
Shipping Fossils *subtracting 4-digit numbers, without regrouping* 15
Fossil Fans *adding 4-digit numbers, with regrouping* 16
Dating a Fossil *adding 5-digit numbers, with regrouping* 17
Identifying Dinosaurs *subtracting 3-digit numbers, with regrouping* 18
Fossils from Afar *subtracting 4- and 5-digit numbers, with regrouping* 19
Tracking Dinosaurs *adding and subtracting 3- to 5-digit numbers, with regrouping* ... 20

Concert Tour

Free Ticket *adding and subtracting 2- to 5-digit numbers, with regrouping* 21
Money Matters *adding and subtracting 4- to 6-digit numbers, with regrouping (money)* 22
A Job with the Band *subtracting 2- to 5-digit numbers, with regrouping (money)* 23
Concert Tour *subtracting 3- and 4-digit numbers, with regrouping* 24
Alexander's Band Van *subtracting 2- to 5-digit numbers, with regrouping* 25
Musical Interview *using* greater than, less than, *and* equal to *with 2- to 5-digit numbers* 26
Bills! Bills! Bills! *subtracting 4- and 6-digit numbers, with regrouping* 27
Putting Alexander on Tape *adding seconds and minutes, with regrouping* 28

Park Vacation

Travel Budget *adding and subtracting 1- to 4-digit numbers, with regrouping (money)* . 29
Picking a Park *subtracting 2- to 4-digit numbers, with regrouping* 30
Summer Visitors *adding 3 or more 1-to 4-digit numbers, with regrouping* 31
Spotting Forest Fires *adding and subtracting 2- to 4-digit numbers, with regrouping* . 32
Counting Critters *adding 3 or more 1- to 4-digit numbers, with regrouping* 33
Forest Products *subtracting 2- to 5-digit numbers, with regrouping* 34
A Tree of Numbers *adding and subtracting 2- to 5-digit numbers, with regrouping* 35

Volcano Vacation

Volcanic Expenses *adding and subtracting 3- to 4-digit numbers, with regrouping (money)* 36
Big Blowups *using* greater than, less than, *or* equal to *with 2- to 5-digit numbers* 37
Blowing Its Top *using* greater than, less than, *or* equal to *with 2- to 5-digit numbers* .. 38
Mountain Climbing *adding and subtracting 2- to 5-digit numbers, with regrouping* ... 39
Earthquake! *adding and subtracting 2- to 5-digit numbers, with regrouping* 40

Answer Key 41

Introduction

Hi! I'm Birdseye. I play the starring role in the Birdseye Math Skills Series. You will find me and my brigade of friends featured in each of these books of Mastery Masters™—duplicatable blackline worksheets designed to give your intermediate students reinforcement and review in basic math skills.

Each Birdseye Math book contains forty worksheets grouped into highly motivating mini-stories. The progress of each story parallels a gradual skill-building sequence so that the interest levels and skills levels of your students rise together.

You can use these worksheets to supplement your ongoing math curriculum in either of two ways. You can duplicate a complete story's worth of worksheets and give these mini-books to your students for occasional review, or you can duplicate individual sheets for reinforcing a particular skill concept. It is not necessary to follow the story lines—each worksheet has an independent context of its own. Although every page is complete with instructions to the students, if you are using the sheets as part of a particular lesson, supplementary explanations or introductory material may benefit your class.

To help you coordinate the worksheet activities with your own math program, the Contents indicates the skills focus for each sheet. Classroom testing has shown these exercises to be suitable for grades 4-6, but remember that you are the best judge of your students' needs and abilities. You may find that a particular worksheet is appropriate for guided work with slow groups or learning disability classes; that same sheet in another classroom may be useful as a learning center activity or as independent work for average and more advanced students. When you have selected the worksheets you want to duplicate, make your own masters or reproduce them on a copying machine. The Answer Key at the back of the book provides a quick check for correcting the worksheets after your students have completed them.

As for me—Birdseye—you'll find me on nearly every page of this book. I'm there to amuse, encourage, challenge, and help your students become more proficient in the practical math skills they will use the rest of their lives.

Name ______________________

SEEING DOTS

When she is not flying herself, Birdseye likes to watch other birds fly. But she has been looking up in the sky so long that she is beginning to see dots. Help Birdseye get a better focus. Solve the problems and connect the dots answer by answer. Soon you and Birdseye will "get the picture."

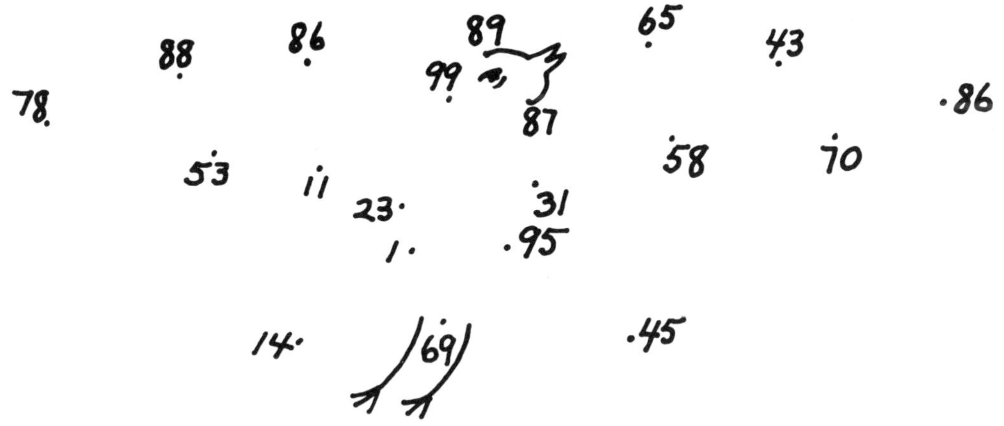

1. 16 + 73	2. 49 + 50	3. 83 + 3	4. 62 + 26	5. 57 + 21
6. 77 − 24	7. 19 − 8	8. 96 − 73	9. 82 − 81	10. 48 − 34
11. 5 + 64	12. 58 − 13	13. 34 + 61	14. 47 − 16	15. 28 + 30
16. 93 − 23	17. 55 + 31	18. 69 − 26	19. 40 + 25	20. 64 + 23

Name ____________________

FLYING WITH THE EAGLES

Birdseye wants to soar with the eagles so she can she how the world looks from high in the sky. Use your eagle eye to watch the signs as you solve these problems. If you score a 20, you're up there with eagles!

1. 54 + 27	2. 63 + 82	3. 95 + 5	4. 71 + 46	5. 18 + 37
6. 116 − 93	7. 73 − 28	8. 100 − 5	9. 108 − 41	10. 119 − 81
11. 24 + 91	12. 104 − 45	13. 8 + 16	14. 150 − 76	15. 97 + 35
16. 105 − 39	17. 30 + 46	18. 103 − 24	19. 75 + 27	20. 30 − 18

____

Name

MEASURING UP

Birdseye would like to know how she measures up to other birds. You can help her by using the chart to answer the questions below.

Height: Birdseye 48 inches
ostrich 96 inches
whooping crane 60 inches

Wingspan: Birdseye 36 inches
albatross 144 inches
condor 121 inches

Speed: Birdseye 54 miles per hour
golden eagle 180 miles per hour
common swift 70 miles per hour

Weight: Birdseye 65 pounds
ostrich 300 pounds

Find the differences:

1. An ostrich is taller than Birdseye. How much taller? ___________ inches
(Hint: 96 inches less 48 inches = how much taller.)
2. A whooping crane is taller than Birdseye. How much taller?)
___________ inches
3. An ostrich is heavier than Birdseye. How much more does it weigh?
___________ pounds
4. The wingspan of an albatross is longer than Birdseye's wingspan. How much longer? ___________ inches
5. The wingspan of a condor is longer than Birdseye's wingspan. How much longer? ___________ inches
6. A golden eagle flies faster than Birdseye. How much faster?
___________ mph
7. A common swift flies faster than Birdseye. How much faster?
___________ mph

Name ______________________

SPOTTING GOLDEN EAGLES

Birdseye is looking for golden eagles. She will see one eagle for each problem below that you get right. Do your best!

Find the sums and differences.

1. 24 + 89	2. 765 − 308	3. 8,109 − 4,675	4. 372 + 564	5. 96 − 77
6. 542 − 363	7. 1,260 + 8,241	8. 38 + 92	9. 85 − 59	10. 492 + 209
11. 7,064 − 1,517	12. 532 + 680	13. 67 − 59	14. 9,286 + 3,579	15. 388 − 279
16. 951 + 251	17. 14 + 74	18. 3,789 − 3,264	19. 141 − 82	20. 2,358 + 7,448
21. 80 − 36	22. 641 + 859	23. 973 − 646	24. 4,563 + 3,737	25. 796 + 582

Name

REPAIRING A TRUCK

Birdseye is visiting her friend Franklin, who repairs trucks. Franklin gave Birdseye this puzzle to solve. First, find the sums. Then match each sum with a blank below and write the letter of the sum in the blank. The answer tells which part of the truck needs repairing.

1. 199 + 768 = A
2. 602 + 199 = B
3. 24 + 48 = C
4. 79 + 15 = E
5. 385 + 376 = O
6. 518 + 464 = R
7. 89 + 32 = R
8. 96 + 89 = R
9. 406 + 237 = T
10. 37 + 85 = U

ANSWER:

___	___	___	___	___	___	___	___	___	___
72	967	121	801	122	982	94	643	761	185

Name ____________________

BUYING AUTO PARTS

Franklin needs to buy some parts to repair his truck. Birdseye is helping him figure out how much they will cost. Use this price list to help Birdseye answer the problems below.

headlight	$9.99
muffler clamp	$2.65
spark plug	$1.13 each
oil	$1.37 per quart
windshield wipers	$4.75 per pair
taillight bulb	$ .84
brake fluid	$3.96

1. How much would a taillight bulb and a headlight cost together? ____________
2. How much would two quarts of oil cost? ____________
3. How much would brake fluid and a muffler clamp cost together? ____________
4. How much would four spark plugs cost? ____________
5. How much would a pair of windshield wipers and brake fluid cost together? ____________
6. How much would a headlight and a quart of oil cost together? ____________
7. How much would a muffler clamp and a pair of windshield wipers cost? ____________
8. How much would a taillight bulb and four spark plugs cost? ____________ (Hint: Use answer to #4.)
9. How much would brake fluid and two quarts of oil cost? ____________ (Hint: Use answer to #2.)
10. How much would a taillight bulb, four spark plugs, brake fluid, and two quarts of oil cost? ____________ (Hint: Use answers to #8 and #9.)

Name ____________________

SETTING NEW RECORDS

Franklin enjoys reading about race car drivers. One of his favorites is Kitty O'Neil. She has set 28 world records in cars and boats. She has driven a race car at 618 miles per hour (mph) and is trying for 750 mph. She has driven a boat at 275 mph and water-skied at 104 mph.

618 is *less than* 750; this is written:

$618 < 750$

275 is *greater than* 104; this is written:

$275 > 104$

Show whether the number on the left is *greater than*, *less than*, or *equal to* the number on the right by writing $>$, $<$, or $=$ in the circle.

1. 54 ◯ 68	2. 91 ◯ 81	3. 36 ◯ 36
4. 167 ◯ 99	5. 43 ◯ 76	6. 60 ◯ 21
7. 15 ◯ 150	8. 834 ◯ 834	9. 269 ◯ 472
10. 925 ◯ 529	11. 617 ◯ 417	12. 308 ◯ 768

Name

DESIGNING A RACE CAR

Franklin is designing a race car. He needs to know how much it will cost to build the car. Help Franklin by finding these sums.

1. Paint
   $\$163 + 207$

2. Fiberglass
   $\$385 + 424$

3. Steel
   $\$797 + 108$

4. Glass
   $\$488 + 315$

5. Upholstery
   $\$537 + 366$

6. Tires and wheels
   $\$208 + 172$

7. Electrical parts
   $\$159 + 504$

8. Transmission
   $\$718 + 235$

9. Fuel system
   $\$338 + 364$

Name ______________________

EARNING MONEY

Franklin wants to build a race car. He is earning money by repairing cars for other people. Below are the bills he sent the people. Find out how much Franklin has earned by finding the sums.

1. Appleby	2. Burns	3. Kingsford
$ 136 brakes	$ 362 body work	$ 446 gear shift
+ 145 tune-up	+ 48 taillights	+ 187 clutch

4. Lincoln	5. Miller	6. Norton
$ 467 air conditioner	$ 216 tires	$ 179 electrical work
+ 57 muffler	+ 24 alignment	+ 65 battery

7. Rice	8. Tuttle
$ 785 valve job	$ 345 axle
+ 109 parts	+ 238 universal joint

BONUS: Franklin needs about $6,500 for his car. Write the sums you found in the blanks below. Then find the total.

1. Appleby $__________
2. Burns $__________
3. Kingsford $__________
4. Lincoln $__________
5. Miller $__________
6. Norton $__________
7. Rice $__________
8. Tuttle $__________

BONUS: TOTAL $__________

Has Franklin earned enough money to build his car? ________

Name ____________

RACING WITH BIRDSEYE

Birdseye is giving Franklin's race car a test drive. You can help her get to the finish line in record time. First find the sums and differences. Then put the answers on the race track. Go fast, but be careful. Watch out for the curves!

A. ____ B. ____ C. ____ D. ____ E. ____ F. ____ G. ____ H. ____ I. ____ J. ____ K. ____ L. ____ M. ____ N. ____ O. ____ P. ____ FINISH!

A. 698 − 237	B. 51 + 40	C. 3,417 + 6,582	D. 9,146 − 5,123
E. 84 − 63	F. 1,535 + 4,023	G. 763 − 451	H. 52 + 25

I. 4,607 + 4,260	J. 25 − 12	K. 349 + 310	L. 608 + 191
M. 39 − 27	N. 356 + 513	O. 78 − 53	P. 9,507 − 8,102

Name

INDY 500

Birdseye made this list of some winning speeds (rounded to the nearest whole number) for the Indianapolis 500 race. The letters *mph* stand for *miles per hour.* Use the list to solve the problems below.

Year	Speed
1910	75 mph
1922	94 mph
1925	101 mph
1930	100 mph

Year	Speed
1948	120 mph
1949	121 mph
1953	129 mph
1957	135 mph

Year	Speed
1959	136 mph
1972	163 mph
1978	161 mph
1979	159 mph

Use subtraction to answer these questions. How much faster was

1. the 1930 winner than the 1910 winner? ________ mph
2. the 1949 winner than the 1922 winner? ________ mph
3. the 1978 winner than the 1953 winner? ________ mph
4. the 1948 winner than the 1925 winner? ________ mph
5. the 1972 winner than the 1957 winner? ________ mph
6. the 1978 winner than the 1979 winner? ________ mph
7. the 1930 winner than the 1922 winner? ________ mph
8. the 1972 winner than the 1959 winner? ________ mph
9. the 1949 winner than the 1910 winner? ________ mph
10. the 1959 winner than the 1953 winner? ________ mph

Name ____________________

AFRICAN CAR SAFARI

Birdseye raced Franklin's car in the Great African Car Safari. She started the week-long race with $500.00 and kept a record of her expenses for each day. Use addition to help Birdseye find out how much she spent altogether. Then figure out if she has enough money left to buy the African mask shown below as a souvenir for Franklin.

EXPENSES						
DAY	ROOM	FOOD	FILM	GAS	GIFTS	POST-CARDS
MON.	$15.35	$ 7.82	$ 3.75	$14.29		$ .45
TUES.	17.21	10.21			$3.00	
WED.	14.92	8.45	1.25	16.71		.15
THURS.	16.44	9.34			7.00	
FRI.	13.89	10.67	1.25	19.45		.30
SAT.	18.76	7.78			1.50	
SUN.	12.57	9.03	2.50	10.11	5.00	.15
TOTALS	$	$	$	$	$	$

Money she spent for:

1. Room $ ____________
2. Food $ ____________
3. Film $ ____________
4. Gas $ ____________
5. Gifts $ ____________
6. Postcards $ ____________
7. TOTAL $ ____________

Can she buy the mask? ____________

Name

BIRDSEYE'S MAIL

Birdseye just got back from the Great African Car Safari and is reading her mail. Solve the problems below. For each one you get right, Birdseye will get a letter from a friend. For each problem you get wrong, she'll get a bill.

Find the sums.

1. 236 + 175	2. 59 + 48	3. 7,084 + 2,903	4. 1,465 + 6,265	5. 60 + 87
6. 372 + 849	7. 4,189 + 1,319	8. 82 + 75	9. 71 + 98	10. 953 + 264
11. 5,074 + 2,569	12. 193 + 433	13. 6,820 + 1,671	14. 871 + 239	15. 42 + 58
16. 483 + 456	17. 95 + 47	18. 2,976 + 2,072	19. 36 + 93	20. 501 + 182

How many letters did Birdseye get? ___________

Name

ICE AGE ANIMALS

Birdseye loves to visit the Museum of Natural History. Her favorite exhibits are the models of Ice Age animals. Look at the museum chart below. Then help Birdseye compare some Ice Age animals to some modern animals.

Ice Age Animal	**Similar Modern Animal**
woolly mammoths had tusks about 13 feet long	African elephants have tusks about 7 feet long
turtle armadillos were about 15 feet long	armadillos are about 2 feet long
ground sloths were about 20 feet long	sloths are about 3 feet long
saber-toothed tigers had fangs about 8 inches long	lions have fangs about 3 inches long

To compare the fangs of saber-toothed tigers and lions, we would say "8 is *greater than* 3." The mathematical way to write this is $8 > 3$, or the other way around $3 < 8$, "3 is *less than* 8." Use these math symbols in the blanks below to compare the animals on the left to the ones on the right.

1. ancient turtle armadillos __________ modern sloths
2. modern African elephant tusks __________ woolly mammoth tusks
3. ancient ground sloths __________ woolly mammoth tusk

Now use the symbols to compare the numbers below. Show whether the number on the left is greater than ($>$), less than ($<$), or equal to ($=$) the number on the right.

4. 36 ◯ 63	5. 752 ◯ 742	6. 4,068 ◯ 9,482
7. 819 ◯ 921	8. 3,695 ◯ 3,695	9. 78 ◯ 45
10. 81 ◯ 18	11. 5,943 ◯ 7,621	12. 129 ◯ 97

Name ____________________

SHIPPING FOSSILS

Birdseye's friend Lisette works at the museum. Birdseye helped Lisette pack Ice Age fossils for shipping to different museums. Use subtraction to find the answers to these questions about the shipments.

1. 9,678 woolly mammoth bones and 3,542 bison bones were shipped. How many more woolly mammoth bones were shipped? ________
2. 8,567 short-faced bear bones and 5,421 saber-toothed tiger bones were shipped. How many more short-faced bear bones where shipped? ________
3. 7,986 ground sloth bones and 4,305 camel bones were shipped. How many more ground sloth bones were shipped? ________
4. 9,788 horse bones and 8,143 deer bones were shipped. How many more horse bones were shipped? ________
5. 6,359 dire wolf bones and 2,034 elephant bones were shipped. How many more dire wolf bones were shipped? ________
6. 7,896 lionlike cat bones and 1,210 mastodon bones were shipped. How many more lionlike cat bones were shipped? ________

7.
  7,986 ground sloth
– 5,421 saber-toothed tiger

9.
  9,678 woolly mammoth
– 8,143 deer

8.
  6,359 dire wolf
– 4,305 camel

Name ____________________

FOSSIL FANS

Lisette sent fossils to museums in several cities. The museum directors wrote to tell her how many people came to see the fossils in each city. Lisette made this list.

City	Attendance
Atlanta	1,342
Chicago	4,247
Dallas	3,601
Denver	2,433
Los Angeles	7,056
New York	7,124
Pittsburgh	5,120
St. Louis	2,101
San Francisco	3,522

Use addition to find out how many people saw the fossils in:

1. Atlanta and San Francisco ________
2. Chicago and Los Angeles ________
3. Dallas and Pittsburgh ________
4. Denver and New York ________
5. St. Louis and San Francisco ________
6. Denver, Pittsburgh, and Atlanta ________
7. Dallas, Chicago, and St. Louis ________
8. San Francisco, Atlanta and Los Angeles ________
9. Los Angeles, St. Louis, and Denver ________
10. New York, Atlanta, and St. Louis ________

BONUS:
Pick any five cities and figure out the total attendance for those five altogether.

City	Attendance
________	________
________	________
________	________
________	________
________	________
TOTAL	________

Name

DATING A FOSSIL

To find out how old this tyrannosaurus bone is, Lisette brought it to her scientist friends. They used a method called carbon 14 dating to determine the age of the fossil. Then they gave Lisette the answer in the form of a puzzle. Help Lisette. First, find the sums. Then fill in the puzzle to find out how old the fossil is.

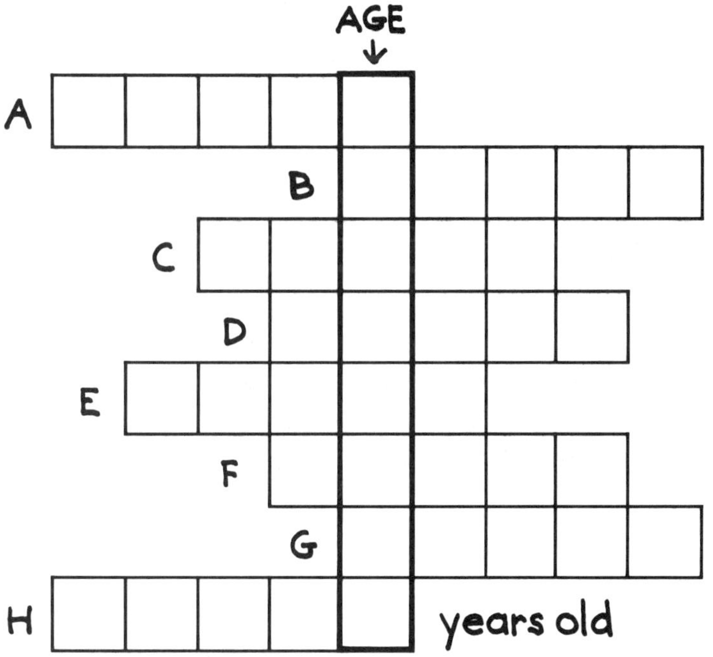

A. $34{,}620 + 60{,}738$

B. $70{,}589 + 10{,}452$

C. $19{,}435 + 59{,}273$

D. $21{,}687 + 68{,}649$

E. $45{,}072 + 41{,}985$

F. $63{,}891 + 29{,}730$

G. $80{,}354 + 17{,}526$

H. $81{,}267 + 13{,}184$

Name ______________________

IDENTIFYING DINOSAURS

Lisette gave Birdseye this chart of names of dinosaurs. You can help Birdseye learn the names. First, use subtraction to solve the problems. Then use the answers to match the names to the correct pictures.

1. brontosaurus

$$\begin{array}{r} 968 \\ -\ 374 \\ \hline \end{array}$$

2. diplodocus

$$\begin{array}{r} 502 \\ -\ 285 \\ \hline \end{array}$$

3. stegosaurus

$$\begin{array}{r} 714 \\ -\ 596 \\ \hline \end{array}$$

4. protoceratops

$$\begin{array}{r} 830 \\ -\ 701 \\ \hline \end{array}$$

5. triceratops

$$\begin{array}{r} 659 \\ -\ 386 \\ \hline \end{array}$$

6. brachiosaurus

$$\begin{array}{r} 271 \\ -\ 124 \\ \hline \end{array}$$

7. allosaurus

$$\begin{array}{r} 403 \\ -\ 279 \\ \hline \end{array}$$

8. iguanodon

$$\begin{array}{r} 318 \\ -\ 165 \\ \hline \end{array}$$

Name ______________________

FOSSILS FROM AFAR

Lisette has flown to Cape Town, South Africa to package new-found fossils. She is sending the fossils to museums in cities all over the world. This list tells how far each city is from Cape Town.

City	Miles	City	Miles
Beijing	8,045	Moscow	6,294
Berlin	5,977	New Orleans	8,316
Buenos Aires	4,270	New York	7,801
Chicago	8,449	Paris	5,841
Denver	9,327	Rome	5,249
Hong Kong	7,373	San Francisco	10,241
Istanbul	5,219	Tokyo	9,071
London	6,005	Baltimore	7,894
Los Angeles	9,969	Vienna	5,671
Mexico City	8,511	Winnipeg	9,054

Which city in each pair below is farther from Cape Town? Use subtraction to find out how much farther.

1. Los Angeles or Tokyo? ______________ How much farther? ______
2. Chicago or Vienna? ______________ How much farther? ______
3. Istanbul or Winnipeg? ______________ How much farther? ______
4. Rome or Hong Kong? ______________ How much farther? ______
5. Berlin or Denver? ______________ How much farther? ______
6. Moscow or Paris? ______________ How much farther? ______
7. Mexico City or New York? ______________ How much farther? ______
8. New Orleans or Baltimore? ______________ How much farther? ______
9. Buenos Aires or Beijing? ______________ How much farther? ______
10. London or San Francisco? ______________ How much farther? ______

BONUS: Which city is closest to Cape Town? ______________
Which city is farthest from Cape Town? ______________

TRACKING DINOSAURS

Name ______________________

Birdseye and Lisette are sorting dinosaur footprint fossils. Did they do it right? Find out by solving the problems below. The fossils are sorted correctly if the number in each footprint matches the last one or two numbers in the answer to the problem next to it. For example, the last number in the answer to the problem next to fossil 1 should be 1.

Theropods	Sauropods	Ornithopods
1. 9,508 − 2,467	2. 928 + 154	3. 4,361 + 6,862
4. 45,725 − 27,451	5. 954 − 679	6. 375 + 241
7. 6,720 − 2,013	8. 7,095 + 4,683	9. 1,310 − 951
10. 24,373 + 39,537	11. 614 + 997	12. 59,478 + 24,534
13. 1,066 − 853	14. 601 − 187	15. 77,510 − 45,895

Name ____________________

FREE TICKET

Birdseye is reading about a puzzle contest in the newspaper. If she wins the contest, she gets a free concert ticket to hear a popular band. The puzzle spells out the name of the band. You can help Birdseye win the contest. First, find the sums and differences. Then match each answer with a blank below and write the letter of the answer in the blank.

1. $87 - 29 =$ A
2. $465 + 106 =$ B
3. $21{,}098 - 20{,}639 =$ D
4. $53 + 77 =$ E
5. $34{,}675 + 12{,}809 =$ L
6. $7{,}642 - 5{,}871 =$ M
7. $121 - 84 =$ N
8. $627 + 499 =$ O
9. $502 - 265 =$ R
10. $34 + 58 =$ S
11. $9{,}588 - 4{,}794 =$ X

ANSWER:

___	___	___	___	___	___	___	___	___	' ___
58	47,484	130	4,794	58	37	459	130	237	92

___	___	___	—	___	___	___
1,126	37	130		1,771	58	37

___	___	___	___
571	58	37	459

Name

MONEY MATTERS

Alexander wants to take his One-Man Band on tour for nine days. He has $4,550 and needs to find out if he has enough money. He made this list of the bills he knows he'll have to pay. You can help Alexander by answering the questions below.

Food	$148.50
Advertising	$1,125.00
Equipment Manager	$432.00
Road Manager	$990.00
Motels	$228.24
Trucking	$695.00
Sound Equipment	$75.00
Costumes	$360.00
Sets	$150.00
Miscellaneous	$225.00

1. How much more will motels cost than food? ____________
2. How much will sound equipment and sets cost altogether? ____________
3. How much more will the road manager cost than the equipment manager? ____________
4. How much more will trucking cost than motels? ____________
5. How much will the road manager and costumes cost altogether? ____________
6. How much more will miscellaneous cost than sound equipment? ____________
7. How much more will costumes cost than food? ____________
8. How much will miscellaneous and trucking cost altogether? ____________
9. How much will the equipment manager and the advertising cost altogether? ____________
10. How much will food and motels cost altogether? ____________
11. How much will sound equipment, sets, the road manager, and costumes cost altogether? ____________ (Hint: Use answers to #2 and #5.)
12. How much will miscellaneous, trucking, the equipment manager, and the advertising cost altogether? ____________ (Hint: Use answers to #8 and #9.)

BONUS: How much will the tour cost in all? ____________ Can Alexander afford to go? ____________

Name

A JOB WITH THE BAND

Birdseye wants to be the road manager for Alexander's One-Man Band. If she gets all these problems right, she'll get the job! How would you do if you were Birdseye? Use subtraction to solve the problems.

1. \$ 10.36 − 7.49	2. \$ .85 − .27	3. \$472.91 − 156.38	4. \$ 3.67 − 3.42	5. \$94.50 − 59.61
6. \$ .28 − .09	7. \$896.03 − 746.26	8. \$ 5.42 − 3.28	9. \$ 76.48 − 43.84	10. \$ 1.10 − .75
11. \$ 57.15 − 9.52	12. \$ .97 − .80	13. \$718.64 − 335.05	14. \$ 5.32 − 1.74	15. \$89.31 − 60.92
16. \$106.43 − 91.68	17. \$ 65.21 − 28.59	18. \$ 9.30 − 7.28	19. \$ .87 − .38	20. \$47.92 − 37.97

Name

CONCERT TOUR

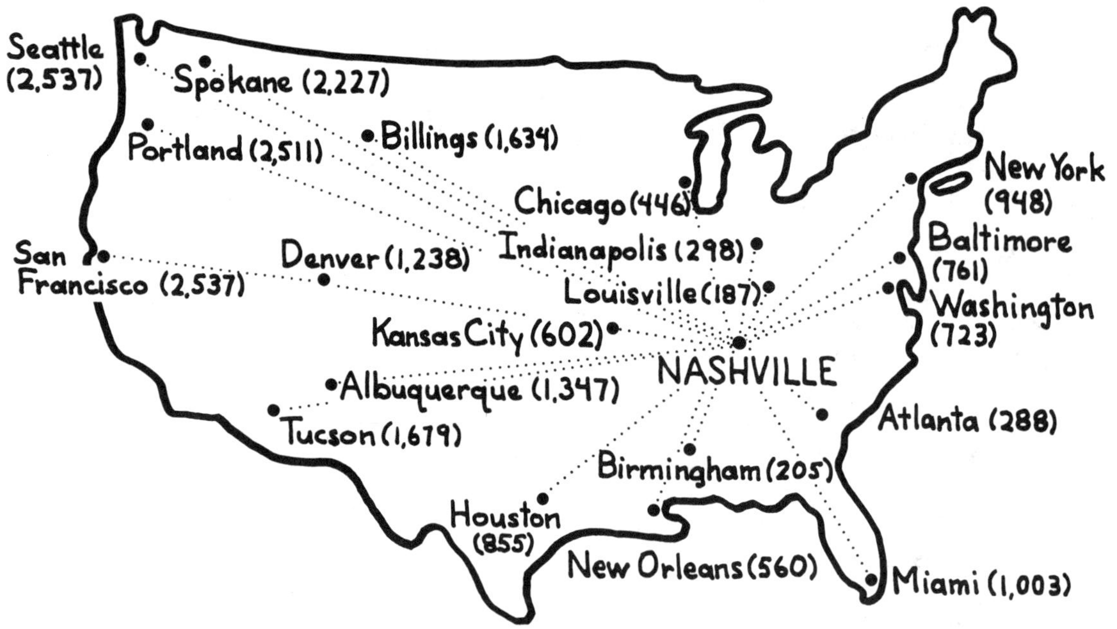

Birdseye is going on tour with Alexander's One-Man Band. They will leave from Nashville. The map shows where they are thinking of going and tells how many miles each city is from Nashville. Help Alexander plan the tour by telling which city in each pair below is farther from Nashville. Use subtraction to find out how much farther.

1. New York or Miami? ______________ How much farther? _____
2. Portland or Spokane? ______________ How much farther? _____
3. New Orleans or Chicago? ______________ How much farther? _____
4. Albuquerque or Billings? ______________ How much farther? _____
5. Birmingham or Louisville? ______________ How much farther? _____
6. Kansas City or Baltimore? ______________ How much farther? _____
7. Baltimore or Washington, D.C.? ______________ How much farther? _____
8. Indianapolis or New Orleans? ______________ How much farther? _____
9. New York or Houston? ______________ How much farther? _____
10. Denver or New York? ______________ How much farther? _____

Name

ALEXANDER'S BAND VAN

Alexander is trying to get everything into his van so he can go on his concert tour. You can help him by filling in the puzzle. Subtract to find the answers. Then put them in the boxes.

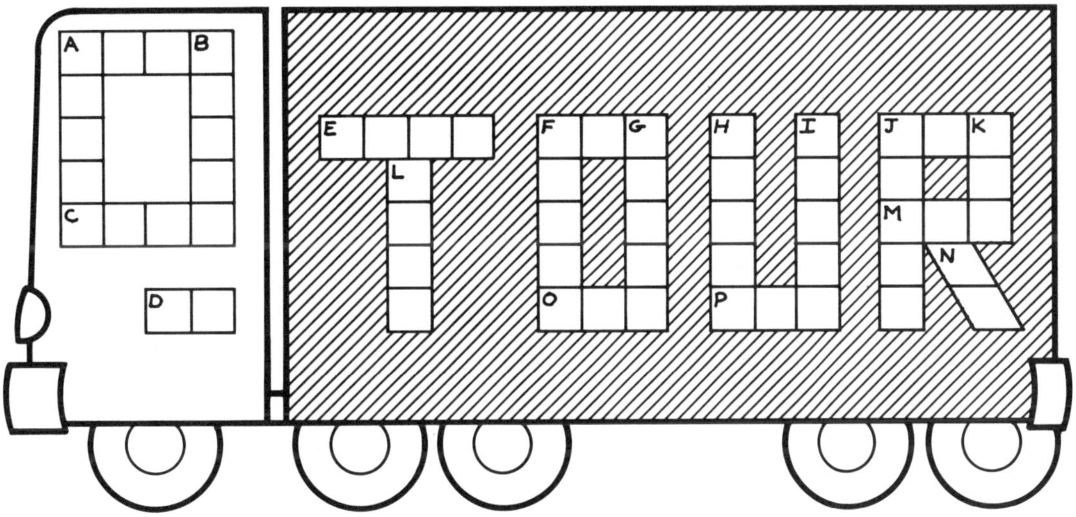

ACROSS

A.	6,431 – 5,273	C.	7,206 – 4,098	D.	57 – 29	E.	8,934 – 6,851	F.	410 – 308
J.	975 – 429	M.	386 – 156	O.	921 – 678	P.	753 – 559		

DOWN

A.	84,263 – 64,340	B.	98,025 – 17,367	F.	50,769 – 32,817	G.	67,102 – 37,549	H.	82,915 – 38,074
I.	28,437 – 11,683	J.	74,945 – 19,676	K.	998 – 358	L.	3,418 – 2,094	N.	80 – 26

Name

MUSICAL INTERVIEW

Quigley, host of "Quality Quotes" radio show, is interviewing Alexander about his One-Man Band concerts. Alexander told him that:

- 35,692 people saw him in San Diego
- 22,857 people saw him in Toledo
- 59,418 people saw him in Miami
- 78,431 people saw him in Philadelphia
- 46,379 people saw him in Seattle

Help Alexander with his interview by answering these questions.

1. Did more people see Alexander in San Diego or Miami? ___________
2. Did more people see him in Philadelphia or Toledo? ___________
3. Did more people see him in Seattle or Miami? ___________
4. In which city did fewer people see him than in San Diego? ___________
5. Write a number that is greater than the number of people who saw him in Philadelphia? ___________

Show whether the number on the left is *greater than* (>), *less than* (<), or *equal to* (=) the number on the right by writing the correct sign in the circle.

6.	54,321 ◯ 38,765	7.	68 ◯ 95	8.	807 ◯ 543
9.	2,489 ◯ 4,289	10.	95,860 ◯ 79,489	11.	1,075 ◯ 980
12.	37 ◯ 21	13.	456 ◯ 198	14.	61,032 ◯ 84,027
15.	784 ◯ 784	16.	3,652 ◯ 5,177	17.	49 ◯ 84

Name

BILLS! BILLS! BILLS!

Before Alexander left on his concert tour, he made a chart showing how much money he *thought* he would spend. After he got back, he wrote in the amount he actually *did* spend. Use subtraction to find out how close Alexander stayed to his budget. Complete the last column in the chart and find out whether he was under or over his budget.

	ITEM	BUDGET	ACTUAL	DIFFERENCE
1.	food	$ 148.50	$ 164.38	
2.	advertising	$1,125.00	$1,096.00	
3.	equipment manager	$ 432.00	$ 375.25	
4.	road manager	$ 990.00	$874.00	
5.	motels	$ 228.24	$ 276.59	
6.	trucking	$ 695.00	$742.00	
7.	sound equipment	$ 75.00	$82.35	
8.	costumes	$ 360.00	$354.67	
9.	sets	$ 150.00	$148.21	
10.	miscellaneous	$ 225.00	$ 302.00	
11.	TOTAL	$4,428.74	$4,415.45	

Name

PUTTING ALEXANDER ON TAPE

Birdseye is making a tape of songs by Alexander's One-Man Band. She needs to find out how many songs she can fit on a 30-minute tape. The length of each song is given in minutes and seconds below. For example, for "Yankee Doodle Dandy," the time is 2:53, or 2 minutes and 53 seconds. Help Birdseye by adding up the times of all the songs. Draw a line under the last song she can put on the tape. (Don't forget—there are 60 seconds in 1 minute.)

Song	Time	Running total
1. "Yankee Doodle Dandy"	2:53	2:53
2. "Down by the Old Mill Stream"	1:39	
3. "Row, Row, Row Your Boat"	2:46	
4. "Clementine"	3:28	
5. "She'll Be Coming 'Round the Mountain"	4:07	
6. "Grandmother's Feather Bed"	3:15	
7. "Grandfather's Clock"	2:52	
8. "My Country 'Tis of Thee"	3:24	
9. "Seventy-Six Trombones"	2:58	
10. "America the Beautiful"	2:35	
11. "Jingle Bells"	3:46	
12. "Oh Susanna!"	1:29	

Name ____________________

TRAVEL BUDGET

Birdseye wants to visit one of our national parks and is estimating her expenses for the trip. She has $754 in her bank account. If she can come back from the trip with at least $75, she will go. You can help her by doing the addition and subtraction below.

CASH:	$754
1. less plane ticket	– 268
2. plus fee for speaking engagement	+ 550
3. less food	– 187
4. less room costs	– 243
5. plus rebate on plane ticket	+ 25
6. less car rental	– 169
7. less gasoline	– 37
BALANCE OF FIRST COLUMN (carry over to second column)	$ ____

BALANCE FROM FIRST COLUMN:	$ ____
8. less park fees	– 17
9. less souvenirs	– 179
10. less entertainment (horseback riding, canoeing, movies)	– 45
11. less guide fees for fishing trip	– 67
12. less film and photo developing	– 38
13. less postcards and postage	– 4
14. MONEY LEFT:	$ ____
Can Birdseye take the trip?	____

Name

PICKING A PARK

Birdseye is trying to decide which national park to visit next week. To help her choose one, use subtraction to solve the problems. Then match each difference with a blank below and write the letter of the difference in the blank.

1. 123 − 68 = A
2. 7,490 − 5,731 = E
3. 6,028 − 2,584 = I
4. 417 − 249 = K
5. 35 − 26 = L
6. 976 − 839 = N
7. 54 − 19 = O
8. 8,541 − 1,369 = P
9. 713 − 485 = R
10. 86 − 59 = S
11. 305 − 132 = T
12. 9,826 − 4,577 = W
13. 92 − 59 = Y

ANSWER:

___ 33 ___ 1,759 ___ 9 ___ 9 ___ 35 ___ 5,249 ___ 27 ___ 173 ___ 35 ___ 137 ___ 1,759

___ 137 ___ 55 ___ 173 ___ 3,444 ___ 35 ___ 137 ___ 55 ___ 9

___ 7,172 ___ 55 ___ 228 ___ 168

Name ____________________

SUMMER VISITORS

Birdseye's friend Juniper Waterfall is a ranger at Yellowstone National Park. She has to get the campground ready for this summer's visitors. She has been using last year's figures to decide what she will need for this year. You can help her by adding up the numbers below.

1. paint

    462
    235
    + 378
    ______ gallons

2. sign posts

    86
    34
    17
    + 53
    ______ posts

3. firewood

    1,450
    2,149
    + 3,682
    ______ bundles

4. tools

    25
    49
    7
    68
    + 71
    ______ tools

5. tents/cabins

    147
    2,385
    + 764
    ______ units

6. recreation equipment

    95
    32
    76
    24
    + 41
    ______ pieces

7. forms for paperwork

    4,673
    7,821
    6,259
    + 5,018
    ______ forms

8. hiking gear

    695
    567
    842
    724
    + 310
    ______ pieces

9. vehicles

    13
    68
    39
    + 27
    ______ vehicles

Name

SPOTTING FOREST FIRES

Birdseye and Juniper are in a fire lookout tower. When the people in a lookout tower spot a forest fire, they call the rangers to tell them where the fire is. This helps the rangers get to the fire quickly. Help Birdseye and Juniper tell the rangers where this fire is. First, find the sums and differences. Then match each answer with a blank below and write the letter of the answer in the blank.

1. 98 − 39 = D
2. 7,304 + 1,958 = E
3. 265 + 467 = E
4. 56 − 39 = G
5. 372 + 267 = I
6. 8,011 + 1,789 = N
7. 750 − 561 = P
8. 4,921 − 3,424 = R
9. 1,369 − 782 = R
10. 49 + 58 = S

LOCATION OF THE FIRE: ___ ___ ___ ___

59 732 9,262 587

___ ___ ___ ___ ___ ___

107 189 1,497 639 9,800 17

Name ____________________

COUNTING CRITTERS

Juniper Waterfall needs to fill in the charts below to find out how many animals live in each area of the park. You can help Juniper complete the charts by adding the numbers down and across. (You will know that you are correct if you get the same answer when you add the totals down and the totals across.)

Place	Birds	Squirrels	Raccoons	Bears	Foxes	TOTALS
By the waterfall	154	42	21	2	3	a
Near the campfire		96				b
By garbage bins	236		54	3		c
On the trail	387		16	1	2	d
Near the cave		13	37	4	6	e
TOTALS	1	2	3	4	5	6

Place	Deer	Frogs	Rabbits	Snakes	Possums	TOTALS
By giant redwood	85	1		1	48	f
By lookout station	14	2			23	g
Near the lake	39	7	469	3	19	h
In the meadow	168	5	258	2	35	i
By the cabins	26	2	317			j
TOTALS	7	8	9	10	11	12

Name

FOREST PRODUCTS

Birdseye is learning about trees. Here are some facts she has found out. Using subtraction, answer the questions to help her learn more.

1. The largest fir tree is about 180 inches in diameter. The diameter of an average Douglas fir is 154 inches smaller. What is the diameter of an average Douglas fir? ________

2. An average two-story brick house uses 10,840 feet of lumber and 1,560 feet of framing material. How much more lumber is needed than framing material? ________

3. One of the largest redwood trees is 44 feet in diameter. One of the largest fir trees is 15 feet in diameter. How much larger is the redwood tree? ________

4. One tropical rain forest receives 180 centimeters of rain each year. Another rain forest receives 500 centimeters each year. How much more rain does the second rain forest receive? ________

5. In 1972, the people of the world used 14.20 billion cubic feet of wood. That year, people in the United States used 5.16 billion cubic feet. How much wood did the rest of the world use? ________

6. The average rainfall in the coniferous forest is 38 to 72 centimeters per year. In the deciduous forest, where oaks, maples, and poplars grow, the average rainfall is 76 to 152 centimeters per year. How much greater is the average low in the deciduous forest than in the coniferous forest? ________
The average high? ________

7. One of the largest redwood trees is 4,304 inches tall. The average ponderosa pine is about 2,400 inches tall. How much taller is the redwood? ________

Name

A TREE OF NUMBERS

Birdseye has learned about trees, but she's never seen one like this before! Help her figure out the puzzle by finding the sums and differences of the problems below and placing the numbers in the blanks.

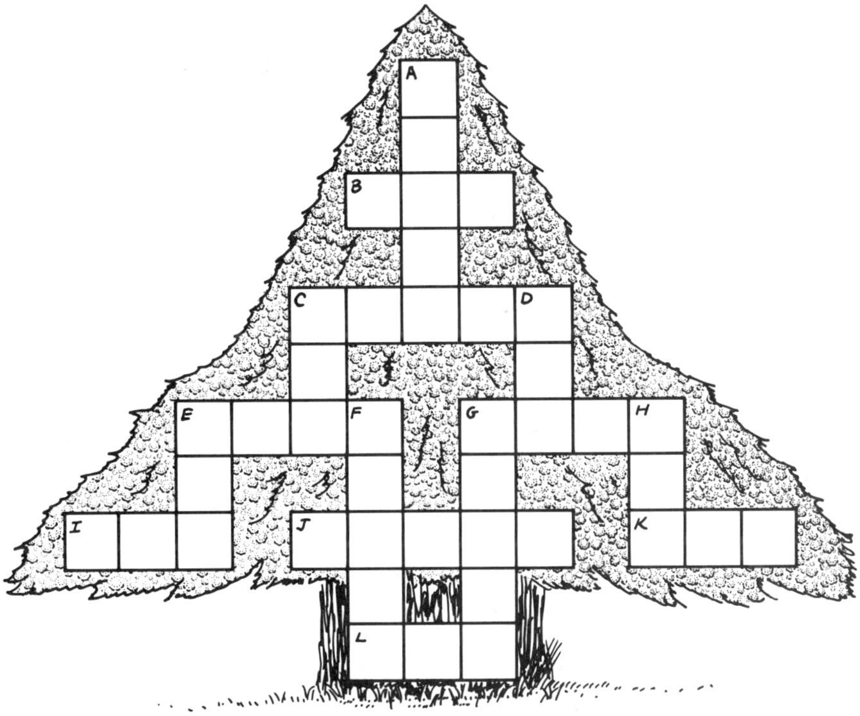

ACROSS

B. 278 + 89	C. 94,355 − 14,213	E. 10,876 − 3,840	G. 1,411 + 573
I. 1,352 − 659	J. 30,481 + 12,086	K. 6,934 − 6,133	L. 365 + 228

DOWN

A. 23,597 + 36,024	C. 469 + 384	D. 752 − 503	E. 1,430 − 717
F. 38,967 + 22,308	G. 65,128 − 54,445	H. 329 + 99	

Name ______________________

VOLCANIC EXPENSES

Birdseye went to Mount St. Helens for a vacation. She made this chart of what she spent for food each day. Help Birdseye find the totals below.

MONDAY
$ 2.65 breakfast
1.89 lunch
+ 6.37 dinner
$

TUESDAY
$ 3.24 breakfast
2.73 lunch
+ 13.48 dinner
$

WEDNESDAY
$ 1.96 breakfast
3.41 lunch
+ 9.83 dinner
$

THURSDAY
$ 3.72 breakfast
2.57 lunch
+ 22.30 dinner
$

FRIDAY
$ 2.80 breakfast
3.75 lunch
+ 10.66 dinner
$

SATURDAY
$ 1.75 breakfast
2.38 lunch
+ 17.54 dinner
$

SUNDAY
$ 2.97 breakfast
15.85 lunch
+ 8.44 dinner
$

TOTAL

Mon.	$ ______
Tues.	______
Wed.	______
Thurs.	______
Fri.	______
Sat.	______
Sun.	______
TOTAL	$ ______

Now, answer these questions.

1. How much more did Birdseye spend on Thursday than on Monday? ______
2. On Friday than on Wednesday? ______
3. On Sunday than on Tuesday? ______
4. On Saturday than on Friday? ______
5. On Wednesday than on Monday? ______

Name

BIG BLOWUPS

Here are estimates of how much dust, ash, and lava was thrown out when several famous volcanoes erupted.

- Mount Mazama (4600 B.C.)—42 cubic kilometers
- Mount St. Helens (1900 B.C.)—4 cubic kilometers
- Tambora (1815 A.D.)—80 cubic kilometers
- Krakatoa (1883 A.D.)—18 cubic kilometers
- Mount St. Helens (May 18, 1980)—1 cubic kilometer

Answer the following questions.

1. Which volcano threw out the most material? __________
2. Which threw out the least? __________
3. Was the Mount St. Helens eruption in 1980 *greater than* or *less than* the one in 1900 B.C.? __________
4. Was Krakatoa's eruption *greater than*, *less than*, or *equal to* Mount Mazama's eruption? __________
5. Which volcano erupted more material than Mount Mazama? __________

Show whether the number on the left is *greater than* (>), *less than* (<), or *equal to* (=) the number on the right by writing the correct sign in the circle.

6.	16 ◯ 53		7.	7,313 ◯ 5,940		8.	284 ◯ 621	
9.	31,488 ◯ 96,844		10.	375 ◯ 119		11.	79 ◯ 12	
12.	6,796 ◯ 4,865		13.	88 ◯ 57		14.	9,603 ◯ 43,359	
15.	715 ◯ 962		16.	77,431 ◯ 80,142		17.	8,124 ◯ 1,256	

Name ____________________

BLOWING ITS TOP

After Mount St. Helens blew its top, it went from 9,677 feet high to 8,364 feet. Here are the names and heights of other volcanoes in Oregon and Washington that are near Mount St. Helens.

- Mount Rainier—14,410 feet
- Mount Baker—10,778 feet
- Mount Hood—11,235 feet
- Glacier Peak—10,541 feet
- Mount Adams—12,307 feet
- Crater Lake (Mount Mazama)—8,156 feet

Answer the questions by circling the correct symbol.

1. Mount Rainier is >, <, or = Mount Adams?
2. Mount St. Helens after it erupted is >, <, or = Crater Lake (Mount Mazama)?
3. Glacier Peak is >, <, or = Mount Hood?
4. Mount Hood is >, <, or = Mount St. Helens before it erupted?
5. Mount Baker is >, <, or = Glacier Peak?

Show whether the number on the left is *greater than*, *less than*, or *equal to* the number on the right by writing the correct sign in the circle.

6.	222 ◯ 401	7.	97 ◯ 71
8.	8,564 ◯ 6,835	9.	42,658 ◯ 27,974
10.	897 ◯ 636	11.	58,573 ◯ 63,296
12.	42 ◯ 64	13.	7,021 ◯ 2,700
14.	359 ◯ 538	15.	9,999 ◯ 10,000
16.	16,111 ◯ 25,000	17.	33 ◯ 25

Name ______________________

MOUNTAIN CLIMBING

Birdseye is flying to the top of Mount St. Helens to get a bird's-eye view of the volcano's crater. You can make it to the top, too, by getting all these problems right. WARNING: Watch the signs!

1. 24 + 96	2. 8,732 − 5,368	3. 965 + 247	4. 70,146 − 47,357	5. 89 − 25
6. 32,674 + 83,159	7. 6,417 − 3,819	8. 7,803 + 2,087	9. 19 + 53	10. 503 − 464
11. 47 − 38	12. 841 + 649	13. 56,817 + 35,487	14. 860 − 399	15. 2,694 + 6,012
16. 92,259 − 62,467	17. 753 + 195	18. 5,842 − 5,175	19. 95,037 + 48,316	20. 521 + 276

Name

EARTHQUAKE!

Birdseye felt a big earthquake on Mount St. Helens. The machine that measures earthquakes is called a *seismograph* (siz·mō·graf). The highest rating an earthquake can get is ten. See if you can rate a ten by giving yourself one point for every two problems that you solve correctly.

1. 8,019 + 8,549	2. 90 − 84	3. 66,813 − 28,973	4. 38 + 97	5. 463 − 162
6. $5.30 − 4.56	7. $401.29 − 400.36	8. $79.54 + 62.97	9. $.62 + .59	10. $368.18 − 178.61
11. 8,702 + 9,038	12. 574 − 296	13. 11,434 − 6,031	14. 1,824 + 7,597	15. 704 + 594
16. $125.00 + 48.00	17. $16.50 + 25.36	18. $212.00 − 173.88	19. $990.32 − 695.67	10. $48.16 − 25.39

ANSWER KEY

Lesson	Answers
1	1. 89 2. 99 3. 86 4. 88 5. 78 6. 53 7. 11 8. 23 9. 1 10. 14 11. 69 12. 45 13. 95 14. 31 15. 58 16. 70 17. 86 18. 43 19. 65 20. 87
2	1. 81 2. 145 3. 100 4. 117 5. 55 6. 23 7. 45 8. 95 9. 67 10. 38 11. 115 12. 59 13. 24 14. 74 15. 132 16. 66 17. 76 18. 79 19. 102 20. 12
3	1. 48 2. 12 3. 235 4. 108 5. 85 6. 126 7. 16
4	1. 113 2. 457 3. 3,434 4. 936 5. 19 6. 179 7. 9,501 8. 130 9. 26 10. 701 11. 5,547 12. 1,212 13. 8 14. 12,865 15. 109 16. 1,202 17. 88 18. 525 19. 59 20. 9,806 21. 44 22. 1,500 23. 327 24. 8,300 25. 1,378
5	1. 967 2. 801 3. 72 4. 94 5. 761 6. 982 7. 121 8. 185 9. 643 10. 122 "CARBURETOR"
6	1. $10.83 2. $2.74 3. $6.61 4. $4.52 5. $8.71 6. $11.36 7. $7.40 8. $5.36 9. $6.70 10. $12.06
7	1. < 2. > 3. = 4. > 5. < 6. > 7. < 8. = 9. < 10. > 11. > 12. <
8	1. $370 2. $809 3. $905 4. $803 5. $903 6. $380 7. $663 8. $953 9. $702
9	1. $281 2. $410 3. $633 4. $524 5. $240 6. $244 7. $894 8. $583 BONUS: $3,809; no
10	A. 461 B. 91 C. 9,999 D. 4,023 E. 21 F. 5,558 G. 312 H. 77 I. 8,867 J. 13 K. 659 L. 799 M. 12 N. 869 O. 25 P. 1,405
11	1. 25 2. 27 3. 32 4. 19 5. 28 6. 2 7. 6 8. 27 9. 46 10. 7
12	1. $109.14 2. $63.30 3. $8.75 4. $60.56 5. $16.50 6. $1.05 7. $259.30 YES
13	1. 411 2. 107 3. 9,987 4. 7,730 5. 147 6. 1,221 7. 5,508 8. 157 9. 169 10. 1,217 11. 7,643 12. 626 13. 8,491 14. 1,110 15. 100 16. 939 17. 142 18. 5,048 19. 129 20. 683
14	1. > 2. < 3. > 4. < 5. > 6. < 7. < 8. = 9. > 10. > 11. < 12. >
15	1. 6,136 2. 3,146 3. 3,681 4. 1,645 5. 4,325 6. 6,686 7. 2,565 8. 2,054 9. 1,535
16	1. 4,864 2. 11,303 3. 8,721 4. 9,557 5. 5,623 6. 8,895 7. 9,949 8. 11,920 9. 11,590 10. 10,567 BONUS: Answers will vary.
17	A. 95,358 B. 81,041 C. 78,708 D. 90,336 E. 87,057 F. 93,621 G. 97,880 H. 94,451 AGE: 88,705,391 years old
18	1. 594 2. 217 3. 118 4. 129 5. 273 6. 147 7. 124 8. 153

Lesson	Answers
19	1. *Los Angeles, 898 miles* 2. *Chicago, 2,778 miles* 3. *Winnipeg, 3,835 miles* 4. *Hong Kong, 2,124 miles* 5. *Denver, 3,350 miles* 6. *Moscow, 453 miles* 7. *Mexico City, 710 miles* 8. *New Orleans, 422 miles* 9. *Beijing, 3,775 miles* 10. *San Francisco, 4,236 miles* BONUS: *Buenos Aires, San Francisco*
20	1. *7,041* 2. *1,082* 3. *11,223* 4. *18,274* 5. *275* 6. *616* 7. *4,707* 8. *11,778* 9. *359* 10. *63,910* 11. *1,611* 12. *84,012* 13. *213* 14. *414* 15. *31,615*
21	1. *58* 2. *571* 3. *459* 4. *130* 5. *47,484* 6. *1,771* 7. *37* 8. *1,126* 9. *237* 10. *92* 11. *4,794* *"ALEXANDER'S ONE-MAN BAND"*
22	1. *$79.74* 2. *$225.00* 3. *$558.00* 4. *$466.76* 5. *$1,350.00* 6. *$150.00* 7. *$211.50* 8. *$920.00* 9. *$1,557.00* 10. *$376.74* 11. *$1,575.00* 12. *$2,477.00* BONUS: *$4,428.74, Yes*
23	1. *$2.87* 2. *$.58* 3. *$316.53* 4. *$.25* 5. *$34.89* 6. *$.19* 7. *$149.77* 8. *$2.14* 9. *$32.64* 10. *$.35* 11. *$47.63* 12. *$.17* 13. *$383.59* 14. *$3.58* 15. *$28.39* 16. *$14.75* 17. *$36.62* 18. *$2.02* 19. *$.49* 20. *$9.95*
24	1. *Miami, 55 miles* 2. *Portland, 284 miles* 3. *New Orleans, 114 miles* 4. *Billings, 287 miles* 5. *Birmingham, 18 miles* 6. *Baltimore, 159 miles* 7. *Baltimore, 38 miles* 8. *New Orleans, 262 miles* 9. *New York, 93 miles* 10. *Denver, 290 miles*
25	ACROSS A. *1,158* C. *3,108* D. *28* E. *2,083* F. *102* J. *546* M. *230* O. *243* P. *194* DOWN A. *19,923* B. *80,658* F. *17,952* G. *29,553* H. *44,841* I. *16,754* J. *55,269* K. *640* L. *1,324* N. *54*
26	1. *Miami* 2. *Philadelphia* 3. *Miami* 4. *Toledo* 5. *78,432 or more* 6. > 7. < 8. > 9. < 10. > 11. > 12. > 13. > 14. < 15. = 16. < 17. <
27	1. *$15.88 over* 2. *$29.00 under* 3. *$56.75 under* 4. *$116.00 under* 5. *$48.35 over* 6. *47.00 over* 7. *$7.35 over* 8. *$5.33 under* 9. *$1.79 under* 10. *$77.00 over* 11. *$13.29 under*
28	1. *2:53* 2. *4:32* 3. *7:18* 4. *10:46* 5. *14:53* 6. *18:08* 7. *21:00* 8. *24:24* 9. *27:22* 10. *29:57 (stop)* 11. *33:43* 12. *35:12*
29	1. *$486* 2. *$1,036* 3. *$849* 4. *$606* 5. *$631* 6. *$462* 7. *$425* 8. *$408* 9. *$229* 10. *$184* 11. *$117* 12. *$79* 13. *$75* 14. *yes*
30	1. *55* 2. *1,759* 3. *3,444* 4. *168* 5. *9* 6. *137* 7. *35* 8. *7,172* 9. *228* 10. *27* 11. *173* 12. *5,249* 13. *33* *"YELLOWSTONE NATIONAL PARK"*
31	1. *1,075* 2. *190* 3. *7,281* 4. *220* 5. *3,296* 6. *268* 7. *23,771* 8. *3,138* 9. *147*
32	1. *59* 2. *9,262* 3. *732* 4. *17* 5. *639* 6. *9,800* 7. *189* 8. *1,497* 9. *587* 10. *107* *"DEER SPRING"*

Lesson	*Answers*
33	(1) *777* (2) *151* (3) *128* (4) *10* (5) *11* (6) *1,077* (7) *332* (8) *17* (9) *1,044* (10) *6* (11) *125* (12) *1,524* (a) *222* (b) *96* (c) *293* (d) *406* (e) *60* (f) *135* (g) *39* (h) *537* (i) *468* (j) *345*
34	1. *26 inches* 2. *9,280 feet* 3. *29 feet* 4. *320 cm* 5. *9.04 billion cubic feet* 6. *38 cm; 80 cm* 7. *1,904 inches*
35	ACROSS B. *367* C. *80,142* E. *7,036* G. *1,984* I. *693* J. *42,567* K. *801* L. *593* DOWN A. *59,621* C. *853* D. *249* E. *713* F. *61,275* G. *10,683* H. *428*
36	Monday: *$10.91* Tuesday: *$19.45* Wednesday: *$15.20* Thursday: *$28.59* Friday: *$17.21* Saturday: *$21.67* Sunday: *$27.26* TOTAL: *$140.29* 1. *$17.68* 2. *$2.01* 3. *$7.81* 4. *$4.46* 5. *$4.29*
37	1. *Tambora* 2. *Mount St. Helens* 3. *less than* 4. *less than* 5. *Tambora* 6. < 7. > 8. < 9. < 10. > 11. > 12. > 13. > 14. < 15. < 16. < 17. >
38	1. > 2. > 3. < 4. > 5. > 6. < 7. > 8. > 9. > 10. > 11. < 12. < 13. > 14. < 15. < 16. < 17. >
39	1. *120* 2. *3,364* 3. *1,212* 4. *22,789* 5. *64* 6. *115,833* 7. *2,598* 8. *9,890* 9. *72* 10. *39* 11. *9* 12. *1,490* 13. *92,304* 14. *461* 15. *8,706* 16. *29,792* 17. *948* 18. *667* 19. *143,353* 20. *797*
40	1. *16,568* 2. *6* 3. *37,840* 4. *135* 5. *301* 6. *$.74* 7. *$.93* 8. *$142.51* 9. *$1.21* 10. *$189.57* 11. *17,740* 12. *278* 13. *5,403* 14. *9,421* 15. *1,298* 16. *$173* 17. *$41.86* 18. *$38.12* 19. *$294.65* 20. *$22.77*

DATE DUE
